GRIMMY AND THE TEMPLE OF GROOM

by Mike Peters

A TRUMPET CLUB SPECIAL EDITION

ISBN 0-590-13568-6

12 11 10 9 8 7 6 5 4 3 2 1   6 7 8 9/9 0 1/0

Printed in the U.S.A.

GRIMMY
AND THE
TEMPLE
OF GROOM

Special thanks to Chris Browne for coming up with the title.

OH, BOY.. MAPS, CLOTHES, SUITCASE....LOOKS LIKE SOMEONE IS GOING ON A TRIP.

GRIMMY, I'M GOING TO VISIT MY SISTER IN ST. LOUIS. I'LL BE GONE FOR A WEEK.

NO PROBLEM....I'LL GUARD THE HOUSE WITH MY LIFE.....WHERE'S THE CHANNEL CHANGER?

NO, GRIMMY, I'M TAKING YOU TO THE HAPPY ACRES DOG KENNEL...

TAMMY BAKKER'S HOG RENTAL?

7/2

C'MON, GRIMMY...YOU'RE JUST GOING TO THE DOG KENNEL FOR A WEEK.

NO, NO

IF YOU'RE GOING TO FIGHT LIKE THIS, I'M GOING TO HAVE TO TAKE YOU THERE IN A CAGE!!

SHE CAN'T LOCK ME UP LIKE THIS, CAN SHE? IS THIS LEGAL? NO TRIAL, NO JUDGE, NO JURY....BUT HERE I AM...

...THE BIRD DOG OF ALCATRAZ.

7/3

HELLO, GRIMMY...WELCOME TO HAPPY ACRES DOG KENNEL....I HEAR YOU'RE A LITTLE HIGH STRUNG SINCE THIS IS YOUR FIRST TIME HERE.

WELL, DON'T BE NERVOUS, BOY...COM'ON, COM'ON, COME OUT OF THE CAGE, COM'ON JUMP, JUMP...COM'ON, GRIMMY...JUMP, JUMP...

7-4

DOWN AND OUT ON BEVERLY SILLS

I'M BEING HELD HOSTAGE AT THIS KENNEL. IT'S TIME TO MAKE MY ESCAPE.

WAIT..I REALLY SHOULD PUT A **DUMMY** HERE IN MY PLACE...

7-19

WHERE'S A CAT WHEN YOU REALLY NEED ONE?

OH, BOY...NOW'S MY CHANCE TO BREAK OUT OF HERE...

I'LL HIDE IN ONE OF THE OTHER CAGES...

THEN, WHEN EVERYONE GOES HOME, I'LL MAKE MY ESCAPE.

ER TBULL

7-20

GRIMMY...YOU'RE ONE SMART COOKIE...

DANGER RABID PIT BULL
CLICK

SO, SIS.... HOW'S LITTLE GRIMMY DOING?

OH, I SENT HIM TO AN EXPENSIVE DOGGIE SPA THIS WEEK...

I'M SURE BY NOW HE THINKS HE'S DIED AND GONE TO **HEAVEN.**

OUR FATHER, WHO ART IN....

DANGER RABID PIT BULL

7-21

Mother Goose & GRIMM

CONTRARY TO POPULAR BELIEF, DOGS ARE IN TO THE HEALTH CRAZE FAD TOO!

WE MAKE SURE WE GET ENOUGH SLEEP.

WE EAT LOTS OF FIBER.

...AND WE ALWAYS TRY TO GET IN ONE LAP BEFORE BREAKFAST.

...HERE'S ONE LAP.

CONAN THE
CENTURION

DRIVER'S LICENSE
OF DORIAN GRAY

Mother Goose & GRIMM by Mike Peters

OH BOY...I'VE GOT A CROWBAR, A FLASHLIGHT AND A COMPASS, THAT'S ALL THAT I NEED.

OKAY, GRIMMY WHAT'S GOING ON?

I CAN TELL YOU'RE UP TO SOMETHING.

© 1990 Grimmy Inc.
Distributed By Tribune Media Services

YOU MIGHT AS WELL TELL ME, GRIMMY, I'M NOT MOVING FROM THIS SPOT...

WHAT COULD YOU POSSIBLY DO IN A DOG HOUSE WITH A CROWBAR, A FLASHLIGHT AND A COMPASS?

WELL, I'VE WAITED LONG ENOUGH, GRIMMY, I'M GOING TO COME IN THERE AND FIND OUT FOR MYSELF...

CITY SEWER

ROBIN HOOD AND LITTLE JOHN

FLEAS AT GOLF

BEAUTY AND THE WILDEBEEST

IT'S LOTTO TIME, MZ. GOOSE.

GOOD, I'VE GOT MY NUMBER WRITTEN DOWN RIGHT HERE.

...AND THIS WEEK'S 35 MILLION DOLLAR SUPER LOTTO WINNING NUMBER IS...

1899618011

NOTHING ON MINE, HOW 'BOUT YOURS?

3-12

MY 35 MILLION DOLLAR WINNING LOTTO TICKET WAS RIGHT HERE ON THE COUNTER.

SOMEBODY MUST HAVE THROWN IT AWAY!!!

CALM DOWN.. IF IT WAS ACCIDENTALLY THROWN AWAY..I'M SURE IT'S PERFECTLY SAFE RIGHT THERE IN THE KITCHEN TRASH CAN.

MUNCH, MUNCH, CHEW MUNCH, GULP.

THE PLOT THICKENS...

3-13

HE DID IT.. HE ATE MY LOTTERY TICKET!!

GRIMM, HOW COULD YOU EAT A 35 MILLION DOLLAR LOTTERY TICKET?

"WELL, FIRST YOU ADD SOME GARLIC, THEN ½ TSP. OF SALT...

3-14

I CAN'T BELIEVE THAT DIRTY DOG ATE MY FORTUNE...I'M OUT 35 MILLION DOLLARS.

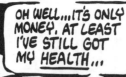OH WELL...IT'S ONLY MONEY. AT LEAST I'VE STILL GOT MY HEALTH...

"AND A ROOF OVER MY HEAD AND ENOUGH FOOD TO LIVE ON..."

I'M STARTING TO SOUND LIKE IVANA TRUMP.

3-22

LOOK, THIS PAPER I WROTE MY LOTTERY NUMBER ON WAS UPSIDE DOWN!!!

SO...WHAT I THOUGHT WAS MY WINNING NUMBER 1899618011 WAS ONLY 1108196681.

3-23

SO, I GUESS I DON'T NEED THAT LOTTERY STUB THAT GRIMMY SWALLOWED, AFTER ALL...

"...YOU CAN STOP NOW, GRIMMY.

MUNCH GULP

FIBER BRAN PRUNES

WEIGHT AND FORTUNE

YOU'VE GAINED WEIGHT AND LOST A FORTUNE.

3 24

mother Goose and Grimm

BY MIKE PETERS

LOBO THE ARCTIC WOLF USES HIS ACUTE SENSE OF SMELL TO LOCATE A BEAR'S CAVE.

SLOWLY, LOBO CRAWLS TOWARD THE LARGE, HIBERNATING BEAR.

INCH BY INCH, LOBO GETS WITHIN STRIKING DISTANCE.

CHOMP   YAH

GRIMMY!

YOU'VE GOT TO STOP IMAGINING THAT YOU'RE A WOLF... DO YOU UNDERSTAND? YOU'RE NOT A WOLF.

OKAY, I WON'T BE A WOLF, I WON'T BE A WOLF...

DUM DUM, DUM DUM,

mother Goose and Grimm

BY MIKE PETERS

9/29

© 1991 Grimmy, Inc.
Distributed by Tribune Media Services

TICKLE TORTURE

HUH?

BONK, BONK, BONK, BONK...

"..EEK"

OH, WOW, SINCE WHEN DID YOU GET A WATERBED?

Mother Goose & GRIMM

BY MIKE PETERS

WHEN I WAS A PUP I HATED CLOSETS.

I ALWAYS THOUGHT THERE WAS A CLOSET MONSTER LIVING INSIDE...

HE HAD A THOUSAND FINGERS WITH SHARP, PRICKLY, LITTLE NAILS THAT WOULD GRAB YOU WHENEVER YOU RAN.

NOW THAT I'M OLDER I SEE HOW SILLY I WAS, THERE'S NOTHING TO BE AFRAID OF ABOUT A CLOSET.

WATCH... I'LL STAND IN THIS DARK CLOSET AND COUNT UP TO A HUNDRED.

ONE... TWO... THREE... FOUR...

©1991 Grimmy, Inc.
Distributed by Tribune Media Services

AGNOSTIC FLEAS

MIME COURT

WHEN ROLY-POLYS CAMP OUT

12-27

I HATE GOING FROM 'REGULAR' TO 'UNSCENTED'.

GRIMMY, IT'S PAST NOON, ARE YOU GOING TO SLEEP ALL DAY?

I'M NOT SLEEPING...

"...THIS IS CALLED TRANSCENDENTAL VEGETATION."

12/29

I LOVE THESE HANDY SIX-PACKS.

12/28

HEY, MAYBE THERE ARE SOME ADVANTAGES WHEN YOUR JAW LOCKS OPEN.

6/21

I'M REALLY WORRIED, ATTILA, NOBODY SEEMS TO CARE THAT MY JAW IS STUCK OPEN, EXCEPT YOU...

IT'S NICE TO KNOW THAT I HAVE ONE GOOD FRIEND WHO REALLY CARES...

"A FRIEND I CAN COUNT ON THAT WILL ALWAYS BE THERE, WILLING TO LISTEN, TO WHOM I CAN CONFIDE MY INNERMOST FEELINGS,

6-22

YOUR TONGUE IS COVERED WITH THOUSANDS OF REALLY GROSS-LOOKING BUMPS.

OH, NO... MY JAW'S STUCK OPEN AND MY MOUTH WON'T CLOSE AND THAT CUTE LITTLE POODLE KEEPS LOOKING AT ME.

6-23

I'D BETTER DO SOMETHING BEFORE SHE THINKS I'M WEIRD...

YAWN

...SO FAR, SO GOOD.

WHY CARTOONISTS DIDN'T LIVE LONG IN THE OLD WEST

THE LOIS AND CLARK EXPEDITION

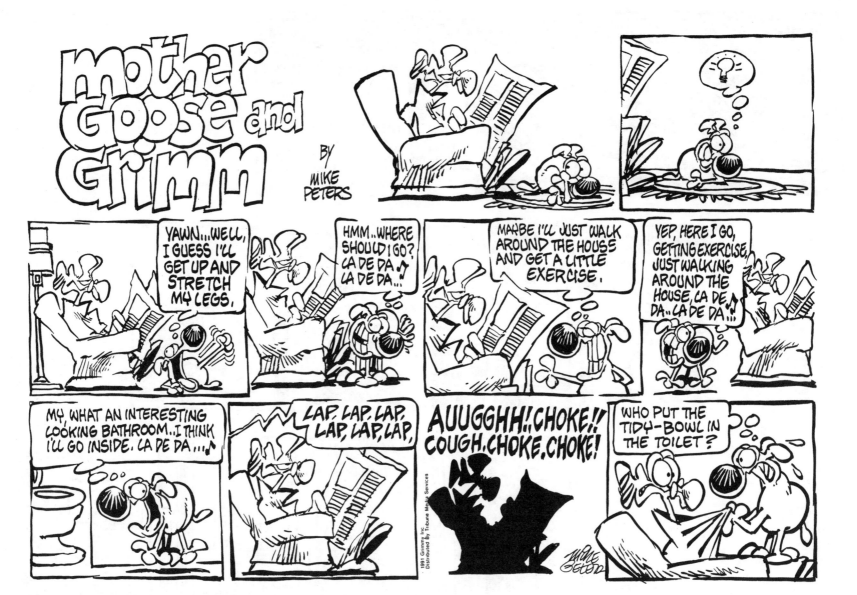

THE GOOD, THE BAD AND
THE UGLY DUCKLING

JUNE 3, 1924, HARRY HOUDINI
LOCKS HIS KEYS INSIDE HIS BUICK

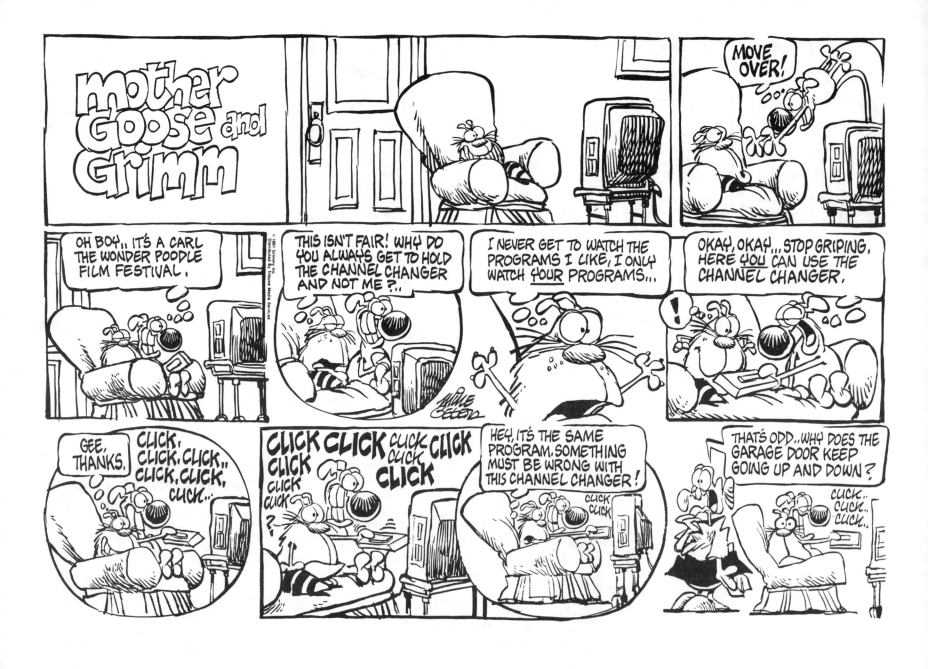

FLEA BARGAINING

PROBLEMS COMMON TO MARSUPIALS

OH, ISN'T THAT CUTE? LOOK GRIMMY IS MOVING HIS LEG, HE MUST BE DREAMING.

DOGS HAVE DREAMS JUST LIKE THE REST OF US.

RIGHT NOW HE'S PROBABLY DREAMING THAT HE'S RUNNING ACROSS A FIELD....

..CHASING A SQUIRREL OR RABBIT OR SOME OTHER TYPICAL DOG THING.

PRAIRIE DOGS WITH CHILI

HI, BEAUTIFUL, WHAT'S YOUR SIGN? LET'S HIT THE HAY.

THE CHEETAH IS THE FASTEST KNOWN LAND ANIMAL

HANSEL AND GRETZKY

THE LONE RANGER AND TORONTO

PUNK ROCKERS

Heeeeeeeeeeeeeeeeere's

™